THE COMPLETE ORGAN PL
CLASSICAL PIECES

Wise Publications
London/New York/Sydney/Cologne

Exclusive Distributors:
Music Sales Limited
8/9 Frith Street, London W1V 5TZ, England.
Music Sales Corporation
24 East 22nd Street, New York, NY 10010, USA
Music Sales Pty. Limited
27 Clarendon Street, Artarmon, Sydney, NSW 2064, Australia.
This book © Copyright 1985 by
Wise Publications
ISBN 0.7119.0757.9
Order No. AM 60559

Designed by Howard Brown

Music Sales complete catalogue lists thousands of
titles and is free from your local music book shop,
or direct from Music Sales Limited.
Please send 50p in stamps for postage to
Music Sales Limited, 8/9 Frith Street, London W1V 5TZ, England.

Printed in England by
J.B. Offset (Marks Tey) Limited, Marks Tey

CONTENTS

SONGS

SONATA PATHETIQUE (THEME)

Beethoven

Registration No ②
Rhythm Unit: **Bossa Nova**

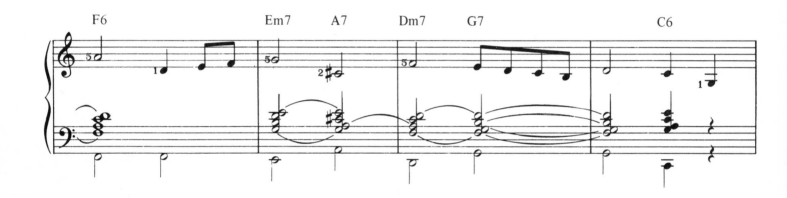

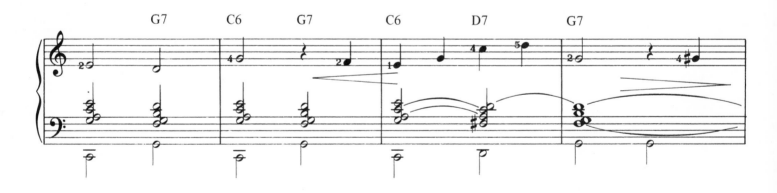

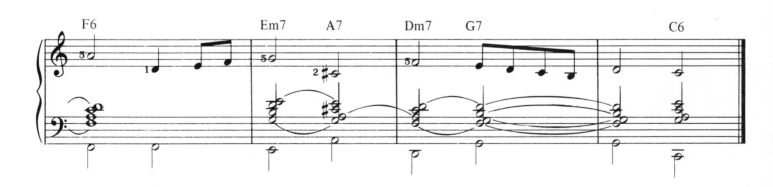

SANTA LUCIA

Traditional

Registration No ③
Rhythm Unit: **Waltz**

SONGS MY MOTHER TAUGHT ME

Dvořák

Registration No ①
Rhythm Unit: **Bossa Nova**

FIRST SYMPHONY (THEME)

Brahms

Registration No ③
Rhythm Unit: **March** 2/4

TRUMPET TUNE

Purcell

Registration No ⑦
Rhythm Unit: **March** $\frac{2}{4}$

ON WINGS OF SONG

Mendelssohn

Registration No ④
Rhythm Unit: **Waltz**

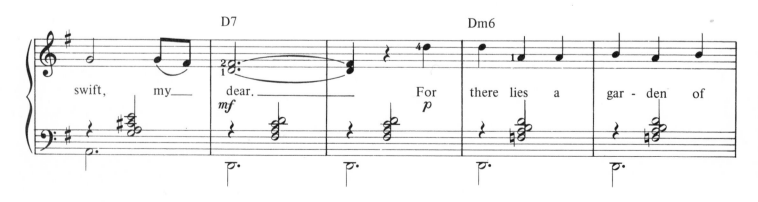

* A♭°, with pedal D

NOCTURNE (FROM STRING QUARTET)

Borodin

Registration No ⑤
Rhythm Unit: **Waltz**

AIR (FROM 'THE WATER MUSIC')

Handel

Registration No ⑤
Rhythm Unit: **Off**

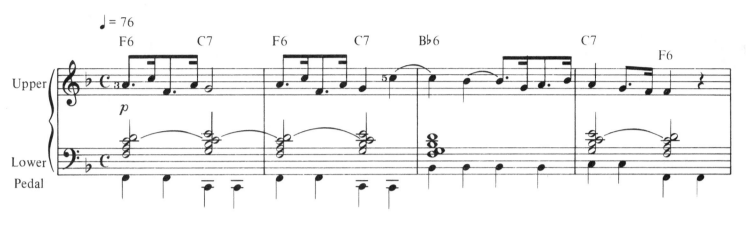

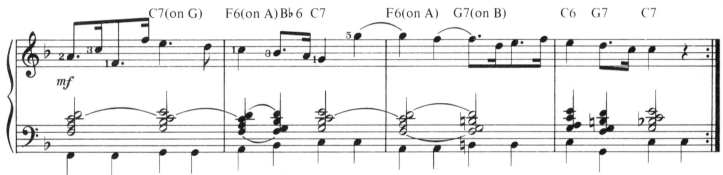

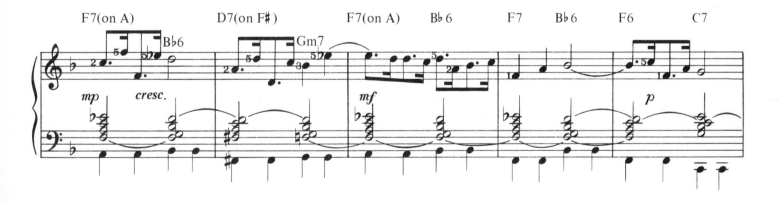

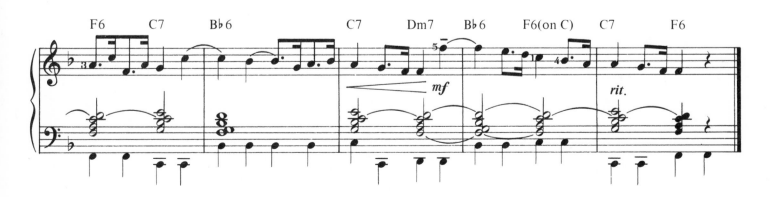

ROSES FROM THE SOUTH

Strauss

Registration No ⑧
Rhythm Unit: **Waltz**

PRELUDE

Chopin

Registration No ⑧
Rhythm Unit: **Waltz**

SOFTLY AWAKES MY HEART
Saint-Saens

Registration No ②
Rhythm Unit: **Bossa Nova**

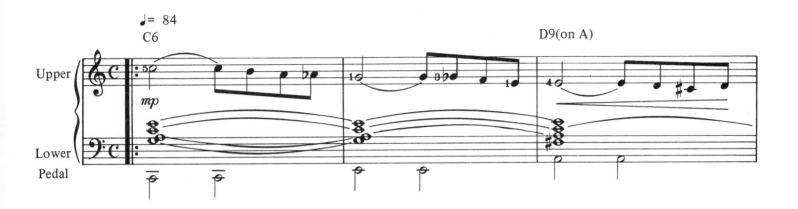

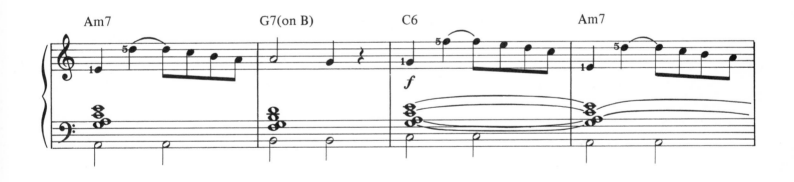

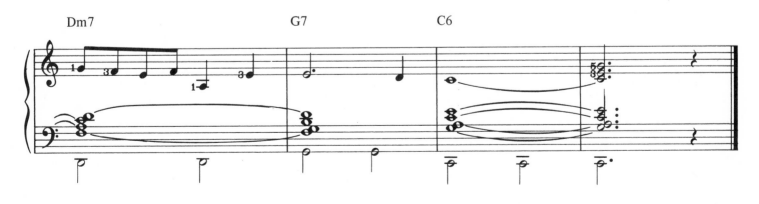

SCHEHEREZADE

Rimsky-Korsakov

Registration No ⑤
Rhythm Unit: **Waltz**

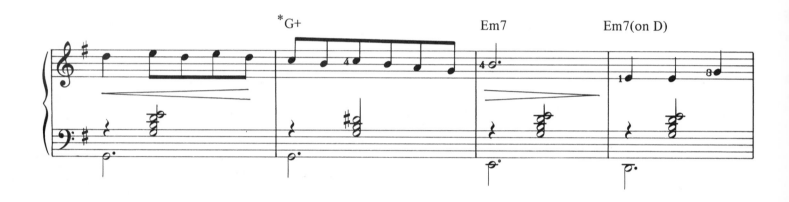

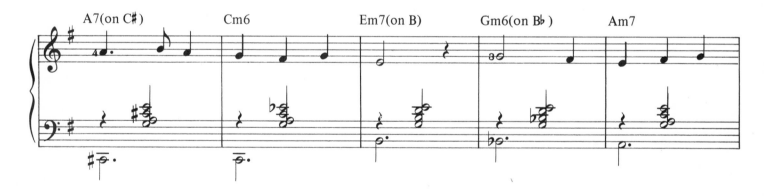

*D Sharp
B
G

LA PALOMA

Yradier

Registration No ⑦
Rhythm Unit: **Tango**

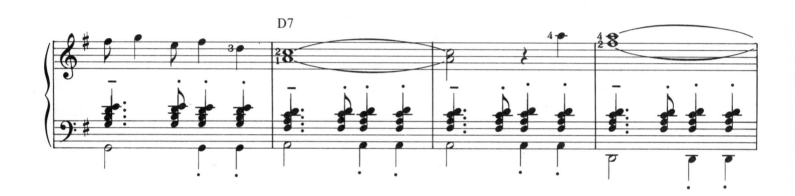

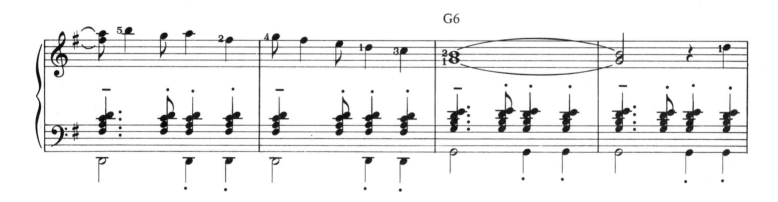

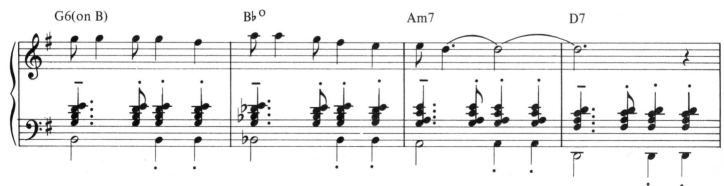

THE SKATERS WALTZ

Waldteufel

Registration No ④
Rhythm Unit: **Waltz**

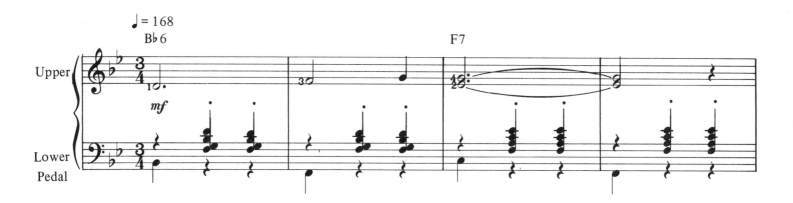

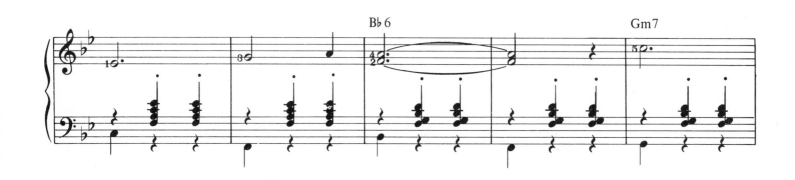

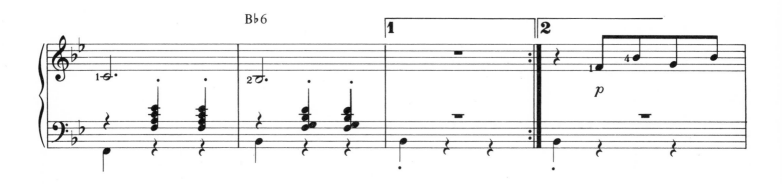

PETER AND THE WOLF (THEMES)

Prokofiev

Registration No ①
Rhythm Unit: **March** $\frac{2}{4}$

THEME

Paganini

Registration No ⑧
Rhythm Unit: **Bossa Nova**

* A♭⁰, with pedal D

O FOR THE WINGS OF A DOVE

Mendelssohn

Registration No ③
Rhythm Unit: **Off** (or Bossa Nova)

AIR ON THE G STRING

Bach

Registration No ⑤
Rhythm Unit: **Rock**

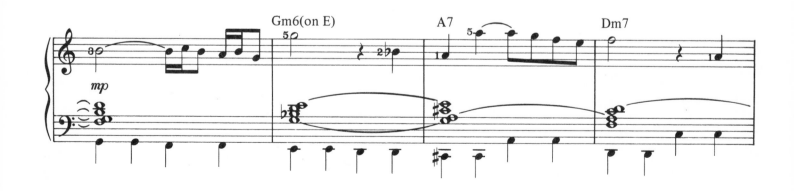

TO A WILD ROSE

MacDowell

Registration No ⑥
Rhythm Unit: **Bossa Nova**

AVE MARIA

Bach, Gounod

Registration No ⑥
Rhythm Unit: **Bossa Nova**

ETUDE

Chopin

Registration No ①
Rhythm Unit: **Off (or Bossa Nova)**

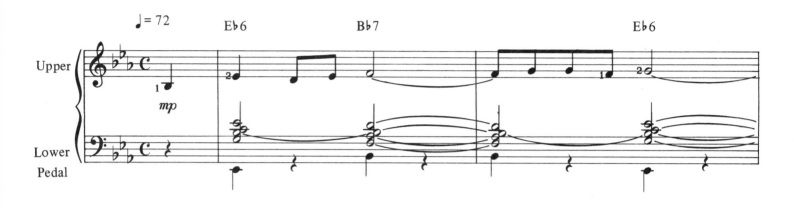

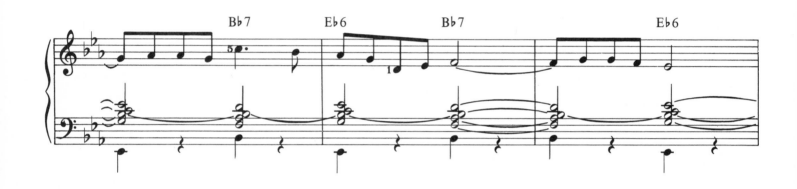

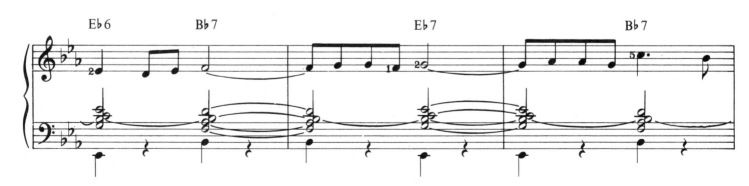

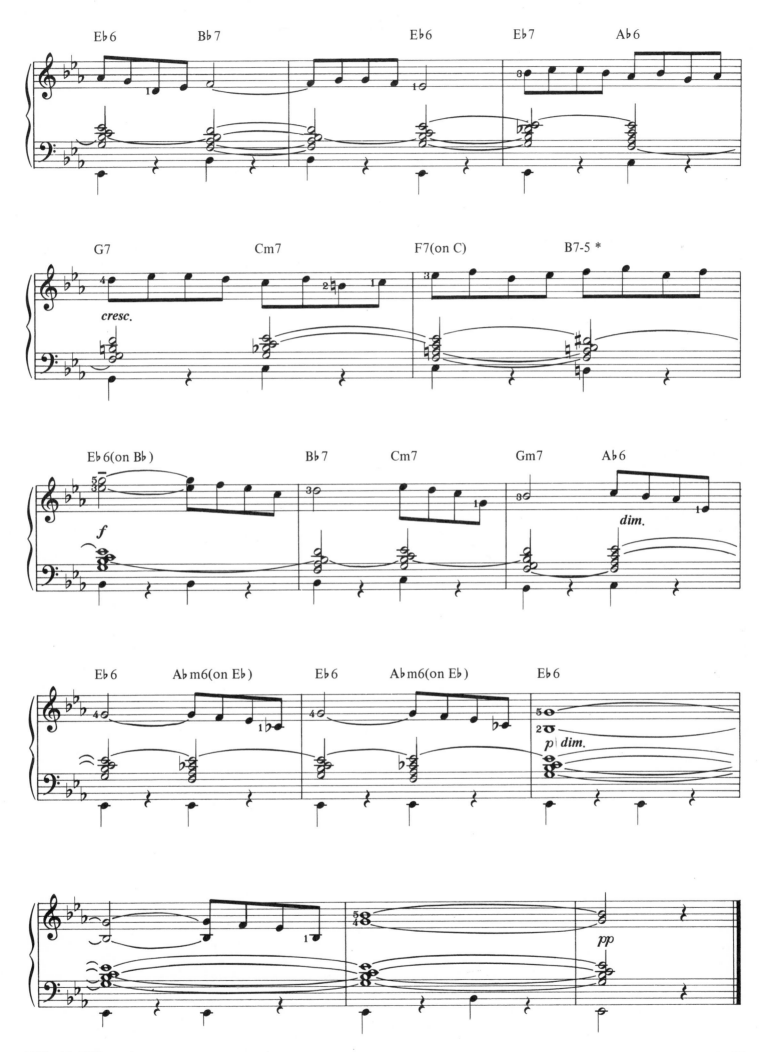

CZARDAS

Monti

Registration No ⑤
Rhythm Unit: **Off** (1st section)
March $\frac{2}{4}$ (2nd section)

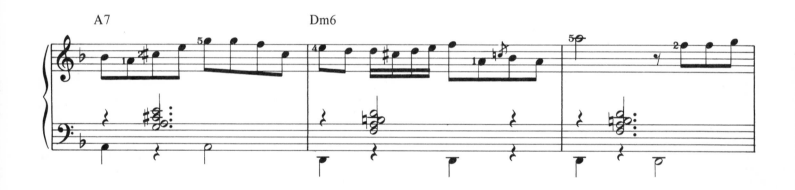

TO SPRING

Grieg

Registration No ⑧
Rhythm Unit: **Slow Rock**

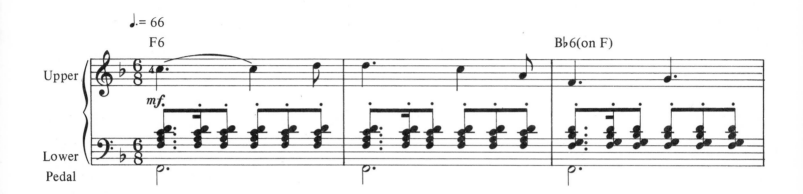

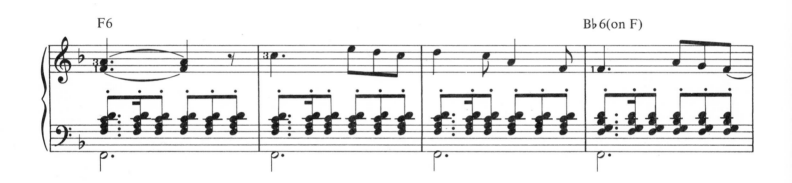

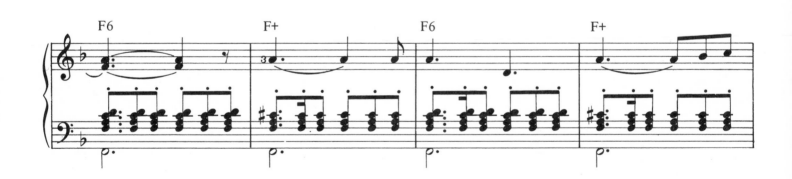

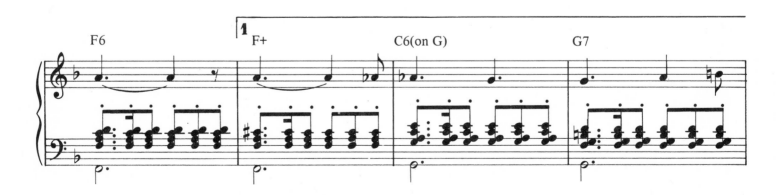

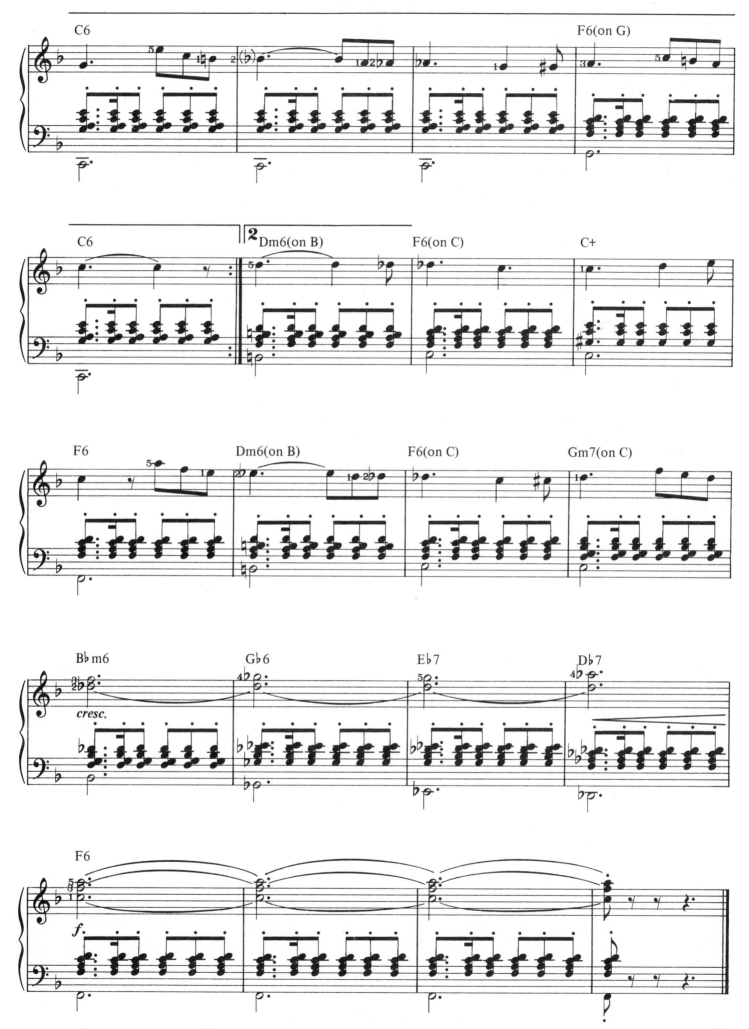

HUNGARIAN DANCE NO. 5

Brahms

Registration No ⑥
Rhythm Unit: **March** $\frac{2}{4}$

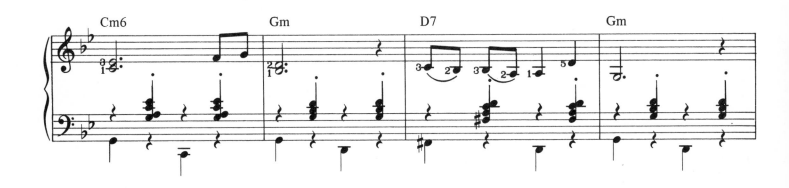

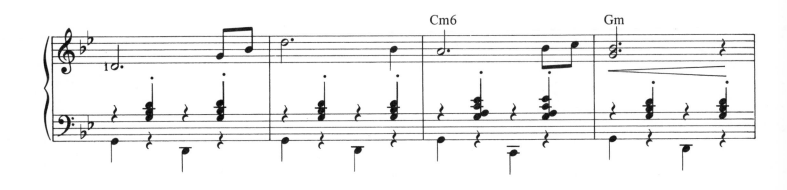

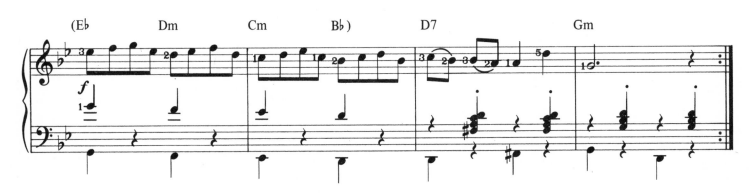

ARRIVAL OF THE QUEEN OF SHEBA

Handel

Registration No ⑦
Rhythm Unit: **Rock**

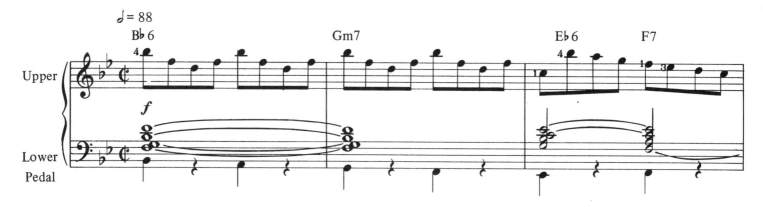

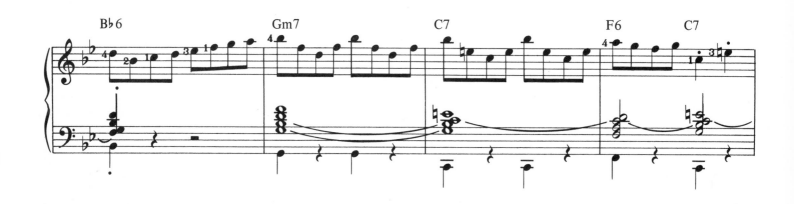

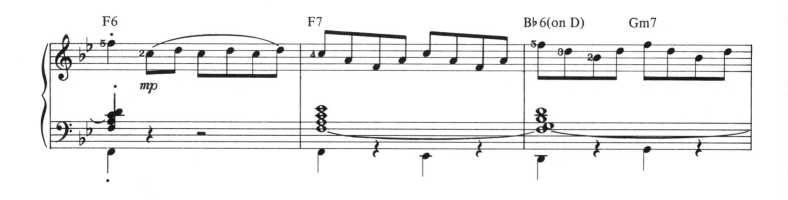

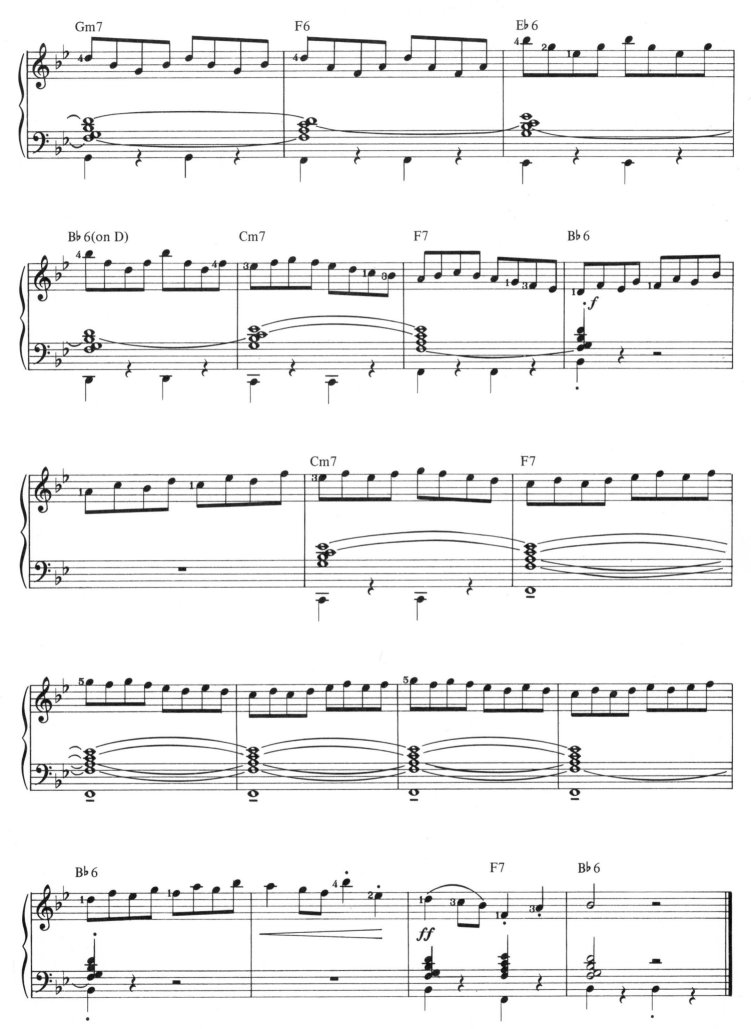

CHORD CHARTS (For Left Hand)

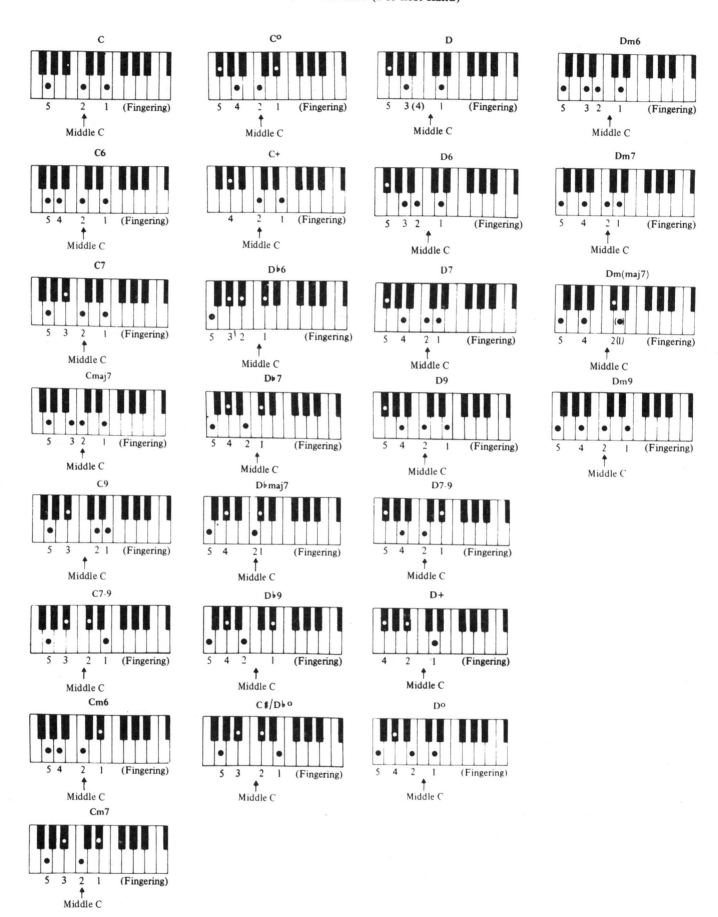

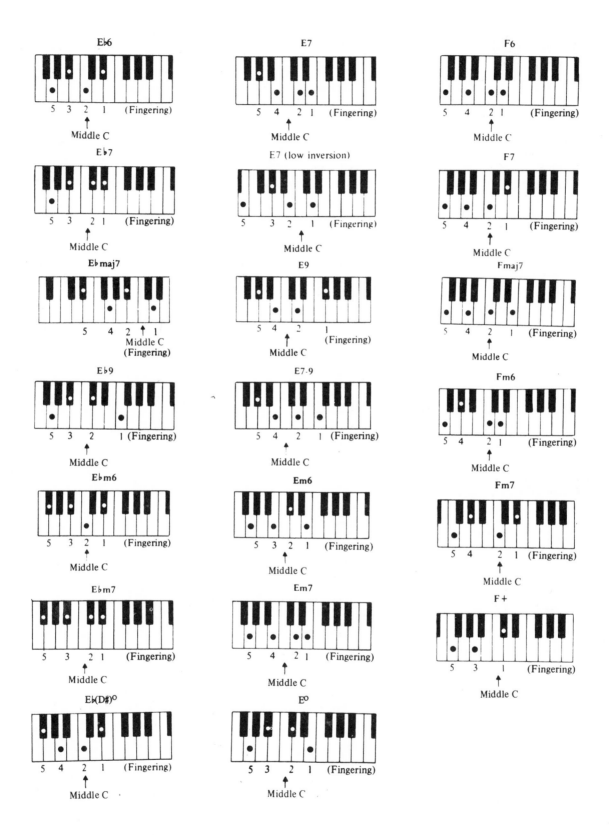

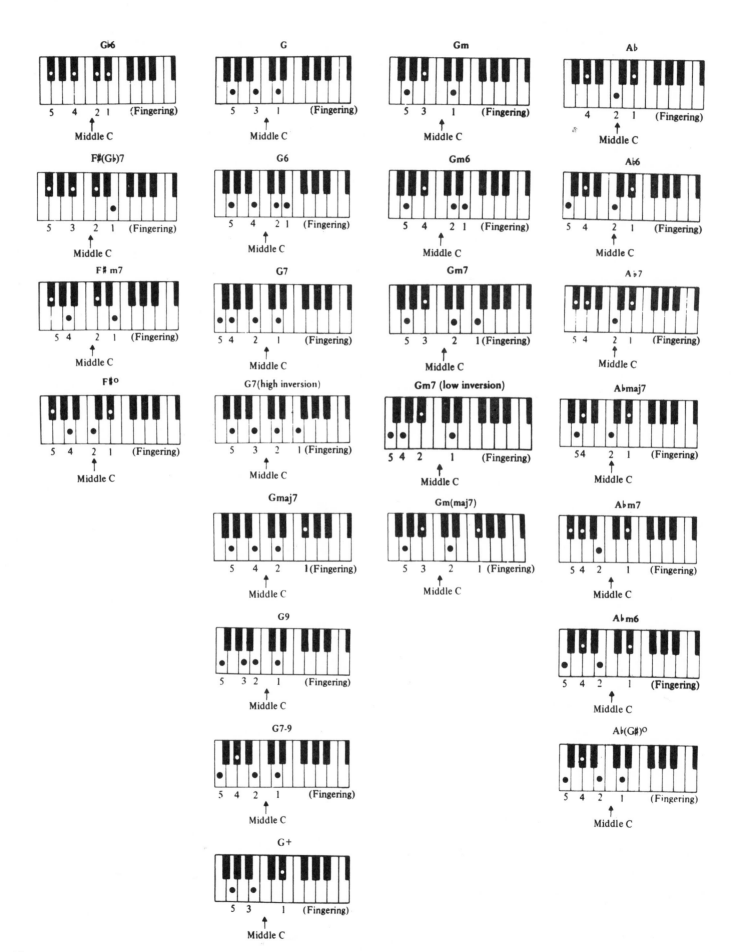

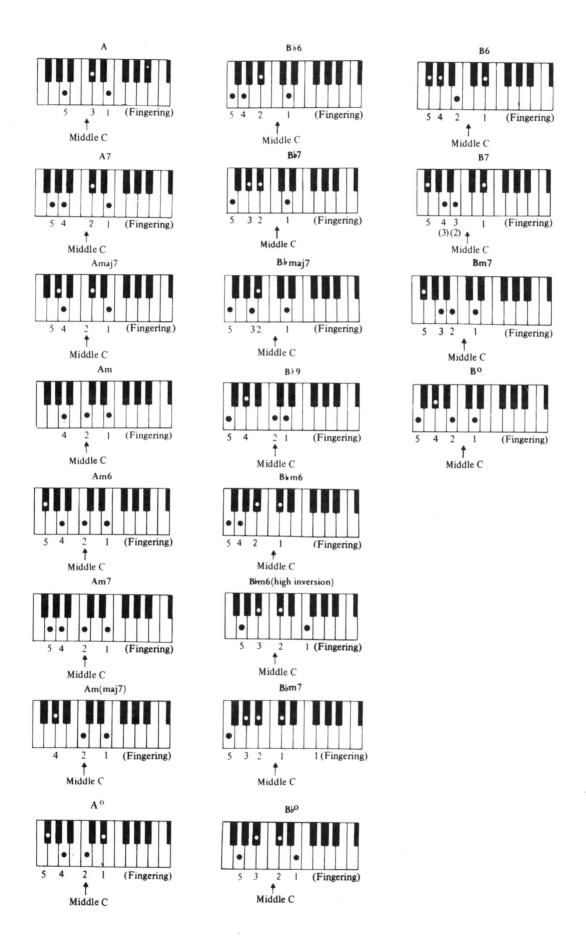

REGISTRATION TABLE
(For All Organs)

GENERAL ELECTRONIC ORGANS

① Upper: Clarinet 8′
Lower: Flutes, 8′, 4′
Pedal: 8′
Vibrato: On (or off)

② Upper: Oboe 8′
Lower: Flute 8′
Pedal: 8′
Vibrato: On (Medium)

③ Upper: Flutes 8′, 4′
Lower: Flute 8′, String 8′
Pedal: 8′
Vibrato: On

④ Upper: Vibraphone (or Flute 8′
+ Sustain)
Lower: Orchestral Strings
Pedal: 8′
Vibrato: Off (Leslie: Chorale optional)

⑤ Upper: Orchestral Strings (Strings 8′, 4′)
Lower: Flutes 8′, 4′
Pedal: 16′ + 8′
Vibrato: On

⑥ Upper: Flutes 16′, 8′, 4′, 2′
Lower: Flutes 8′, 4′, String 8′
Pedal: 16′ + 8′
Vibrato: On (or Leslie: Tremolo)

⑦ Upper: Brass Ensemble (Trombone 16′,
Trumpet 8′)
Lower: Flutes 8′, 4′
Pedal: 16′ + 8′
Vibrato: On

⑧ Upper: Flutes 16′, 8′, 4′ + Piano
Lower: Orchestral Strings
Pedal: 16′ + 8′
Vibrato: On (or Leslie: Tremolo)

DRAWBAR ORGANS

① Upper: 00 7272 420
Lower: (00)5402 000(0)
Pedal: 4-(2)
Vibrato: On (or Off)

② Upper: 00 3600 200
Lower: (00)6431 100(0)
Pedal: 4-(2)
Vibrato: On (Medium)

③ Upper: 00 7500 000
Lower: (00)5443 211(0)
Pedal: 4-(2)
Vibrato: On

④ Upper: 00 8600 000
+ Sustain
Lower: (00)5333 221(0)
Pedal: 4-(2)
Vibrato: Off (Leslie: Chorale optional)

⑤ Upper: 40 8757 234
Lower: (00)7605 000(0)
Pedal: 6-(3)
Vibrato: On

⑥ Upper: 88 8004 007
Lower: (00)6554 044(0)
Pedal: 6-(3)
Vibrato: On (or Leslie: Tremolo)

⑦ Upper: 66 8555 400
Lower: (00)8604 000(0)
Pedal: 6-(3)
Vibrato: On

⑧ Upper: 80 8606 006 + Piano
Lower: (00)5333 222(0)
Pedal: 5-(3)
Vibrato: On (or Leslie: Tremolo)